THE KING'S MAGICIANS

Quran Stories for Little Hearts

by

SANIYASNAIN KHAN

The Prophet Musa عَلَيْهِ السَّلَام was one of the great prophets who lived in Egypt about 4000 years ago. During his time Egypt was ruled by a tyrant king known as Firawn or Pharaoh.

Allah gave the Prophet Musa عليه السلام several miracles and asked him to go to Firawn with these signs and give His message to Firawn, who had made himself a tyrant in the land.

The Prophet Musa عليه السلام threw down his staff and it turned into a big snake. Then he drew out his hand out of his armpit, and it was shining brightly. But Firawn rejected these miracles, calling them magic.

Firawn called his best magicians to outdo the Prophet Musa ﷺ. When the magicians threw down their ropes and sticks, they looked like snakes of all sizes. Musa ﷺ was horrified, as the snakes seemed to coil and uncoil around him.

But Allah commanded Musa ﷺ to throw down his staff. As Musa ﷺ did so, all of a sudden, it became a huge snake. What was more amazing was that it began to eat up all the other snakes one after another, until it had eaten them all up.

Everyone was wonderstruck. The magicians fell on the ground in adoration, exclaiming, "We believe in the Lord of Musa and Harun!"

The people who followed Firawn wanted him to kill Musa ﷺ. One of his follower's was Qarun (or Korah) he was very rich and had lots of treasure. But when Musa ﷺ prayed against him, Qarun's house with all his treasures sank into the earth.

Firawn was not able to harm the Prophet Musa ﷺ. But he soon redoubled his torment on the Banu Israel tribe.

When the tyranny of Firawn became unbearable, Allah guided the Prophet Musa ﷺ to move out of Egypt with the entire tribe of the Children of Israel.

But Firawn pursued the caravan. As the Prophet Musa عليه السلام reached the shore of the Red Sea, the army of Firawn came very near to crushing the Children of Israel.

But due to a miracle of Allah, the sea split
in two halves and the caravan safely
reached the other side the sea.

21

Firawn and his mighty army wanted to punish the Prophet Musa علیه السلام and his people. They also set their feet on the special path created by Allah for the Children of Israel. But as the army reached in the middle of the sea, the sea waves fell on them and everyone was drowned.

The Prophet Musa ﷺ and the Children of Israel thanked Allah for saving them from the tyrant king, Firawn.

With patience and trust in Allah, believers can overcome any hardship they face in their lives.

Find Out More
To know more about the message and meaning of Allah's words, look up the following parts of the Quran which tell the story of the Prophet Musa ﷺ.
Surah al-Araf 7:109-126, *Surah al-Shuara* 26:52-67

ﷺ *Alayhis Salam* 'May peace be upon him.'
The customary blessings on the prophets.